for Andrew & Christine

The "FOREVER FRIENDS" FRIENDSHIP Book

by
.Deborah Jones.

First published in 1991
by Brownsword Books
28 Gay Street, Bath, England

Printed and bound in Great Britain by
William Clowes Limited, Beccles and London

ISBN 1 873615 03 5

To Syl

from David

True Friendship is hard to find....

...but once found , ...

.....it's a Joy to keep!

When Friends meet,
Hearts Warm!

The Road to
a friend's House
is never too long

A True Friend is the Best Possession.

Old Wine,
   Old Books,
      Old friends
         ... are best!

There is only
One way.....

....to keep
a friend......

.....and that is to be One !

Friendship is something
precious shared.

Happy Days spent together,
Become Memories for friends
to treasure.

When others can only talk .....

.... a friend knows when to Listen .

Friends Forever!